The Magical Universe

*Answering the Call of Climate Change
for Personal and Global Transformation*

Bruce McGraw

Printed in the United States of America

First Printing, 2022

ISBN: 978-1-7377371-0-0 (p)
ISBN: 978-1-7377371-1-7 (e)

Publisher: Bruce McGraw | https://www.bruce-mcgraw.com/

Edited by: Nina Shoroplova
Cover Design: Angie Alaya

Book Design: Amit Dey

"There are only two ways to live your life.
One is as though nothing is a miracle.
The other is as though everything
is a miracle."

—Albert Einstein

"There is nothing more powerful than an
idea whose time has come."

—Victor Hugo

Praise for *The Magical Universe*

From his powerful opening paragraph, Bruce McGraw makes clear the urgency of his concern that climate change is irreversibly altering our world for the worse. This is a book that needs to be widely read and heeded.

—**Ira Rifkin**,
author of *Spiritual Perspectives on Globalization*.

The Magical Universe is written in a wonderfully engaging style that's easy to read and draws you in -- honestly, it slides right down. I don't remember ever being treated to a survey of philosophy and its logical trajectory in such an engaging and easy to understand style.

—**Jennifer Morgan**,
author, *Universe Story Trilogy* (*Born with a Bang, From Lava to Life, Mammals Who Morph*); and president, DTNetwork.org.

The Magical Universe is a feast of ideas, served in perfect proportions. His thesis is simple and direct: if we don't wake up from our debilitating unconsciousness and realize the sacred miracle of our own existence, we will lose it all. Once you get a taste, you won't stop till you get your fill.

—Peter Bolland,
Professor of Philosophy and Humanities,
Southwestern College and author of
*The Seven Stone Path: A
n Everyday Journey to Wisdom*

Readers of *The Magical Universe* will be left with a greater appreciation for the stunning miracles that led to the creation of the universe, and the relationship between personal evolution and the climate change crisis.

—David Mercier,
author, *A Beautiful Medicine*

The Magical Universe has me asking more questions and given me more appreciation for the impact that we can all have to preserve and protect our beautiful planet and universe moving forward – consciously that is.

—Emily M Moore,
Executive Director,
Cabrillo National Monument Foundation

The Magical Universe offers us perspective, meaning, and appreciation for our lives and the rediscovery of the cosmic magic happening around and inside us in each moment.

—Stephan Martin,
astronomer, educator, and author of
Cosmic Conversations: Dialogues on the Nature of the Universe and the Search for Reality

Anyone embarking on the journey of awakening or deepening their path will benefit from this potent book. *The Magical Universe* is a healing balm for the Soul.

—Diane dhiana sage Barnes,
co-author of *Sovereign* and *Jaguar*; and
CEO of Mindful Living Studio Global.

McGraw has meshed the style of storytelling with scientific writing that brings forth waves of scientific facts to explain how we can live in both a rational and magical universe. He claims that when we understand this, then we have the key to deal with Climate Change and all our other problems. Give it a read and see if you agree.

—Sohel Bahjat
author of *Secularism in Eastern Eyes* and
Criticism of the Muslim Mind.

This book may be of special interest to those who are drawn to the study of the physical evolution of the universe, including earth, and who may be open to consider that there is a deeper Reality and consciousness that has a vital bearing on the issue of both evolution in its different aspects and present day climate change.

—Joseph Edmonds,
Adjunct Professor of Religious Studies,
Grossmont College (retired)

The Magical Universe

For more information on The Magical Universe
and to sign up for the email list visit
www.bruce-mcgraw.com.

Contents

Introduction

The title of this book, *The Magical Universe*, may sound strange. It may strike some as childish and immature, perhaps a book for children or unsophisticated people, but I assure you it is not. It is completely serious and for the curious, the intelligent, and the open-minded.

You see, we have a lot of problems on this planet, and if we don't change our worldview we aren't going to be able to solve them. In fact, a recent UN Climate Change report says if we don't drastically cut our use of fossil fuels, then life on this planet will become very difficult by 2030.[1] This means wildfires, flooding, drought, and hurricanes will occur more often and with greater devastation. Also insects—essential for crop pollination—will be

---

[1] https://thehill.com/policy/energy-environment/410343-world-needs-unprecedented-efforts-to-avoid-key-global-warming-level

affected, potentially leading to food scarcity, and all this is only eight years away.

One of our biggest problems is we have lost that childlike way of viewing the world as magical. To many adults, the world is just mundane, predictable, and for the most part dead. We've seen it all and know it all. Nothing can surprise us anymore and this makes us cynical and angry as though somehow we have been dealt a bill of goods. A world that once teemed with possibilities when we were young, has turned out to be one big joke on us. There's no Santa Claus, Easter Bunny, or happily ever after. It's all been one big fat lie and we're pissed off and "By God, somebody is going to have to pay for this con job!"

Much of humanity has this problem of perspective—we cannot see the big picture, only the personal one—and that short-sightedness is threatening our very ability to exist on this planet. We are so wrapped up in our pain, ego and lust for more, that all we want to do is lash out at the world. The world has lied to us and we are mad as hell and we aren't going to take it anymore.

But if we could just step back for a minute, put away our smartphones, stop texting, get off Facebook or whatever diversions we regularly indulge in, and look at things a little more objectively, with a little more detachment, we will see it just isn't so. The world hasn't lied to us; our perspective has. It's not the world that is the problem but our perspective of the world that is the problem.

As someone once said, "If it is the world that is out of whack then we have no hope because there is nothing we can do about that. However, if it is ourselves who are out of whack, then there is something we can do: we can change ourselves and our worldview."

That is what *The Magical Universe* calls us to do. We need to recapture our inner child that sees life as magical. It was Jesus who said, "Truly I say to you, unless you are converted and become like children, you will not enter the kingdom of heaven."

I'm not talking about returning to a childish way of viewing things—we couldn't do that if we wanted. Instead, I'm talking about rekindling that creative spark that would allow us once again to view life as magical.

There are two kinds of innocence: a childish innocence and a mature innocence. I am referring to the latter. To attain that state, we have to rediscover the mystery of life we had as children, but from an adult's perspective. We can no longer view it from a childish perspective because we have experienced too much to go back and pretend we haven't. No, the way is forward, through all our pain and misery, to allow a new state of being to emerge that will rekindle a magical view of life.

Look at it as though we are taking off in an airplane in the middle of a city that has a dense layer of smog hovering over it. As we take off, everything looks gloomy because the smog blocks out the sun. This represents our current state of mind. As the plane rises, we enter into the pollution and, for a while, we can't see anything. Even our gloomy view is cut off. If we didn't know better, we would think it would have been better to stay beneath the smog because at least we could see something.

Now we see nothing.

Eventually though, we will break through the smog and the pollution and move into the bright sunshine that was there all the time, just waiting for us. Now everything is crystal clear and beautiful.

This is the breakthrough to our true Self.

To get this clear view, we had to take a step back before we could leap forward to a new vision. Only with new sight can we tackle the myriad of problems before us, the most serious being Climate Change because it threatens our very ability to survive on this planet—as the recent UN report verifies.

Climate Change is the perfect vehicle through which we can reclaim our lost innocence. Think about it. Why don't we like to deal with Climate Change? Why does the media virtually ignore it, even when super fires, floods, and droughts continue to occur, each growing more and more devastating as the climate heats up?

It is because climate change is such a big issue, such a scary issue, that nobody wants to face it.

However, I don't believe climate change is the actual problem here, but rather it's our reaction to climate change that's the problem. What do I mean by this? The problem is the thoughts and feeling we encounter when we attempt to think about climate change. We know it is terrible and potentially devastating, but we feel helpless to do anything about it. It conjures up all sorts of uncomfortable feelings that we don't want to confront.

So, to deal with climate change, we have to deal with ourselves. But that is precisely why climate change is so perfect for our growth and transformation. It forces us to face all the pain and misery inside us. And that is exactly what we have to do if we want to climb out of our jaded worldview and into a more magical one.

In short, climate change is the universe's way of waking us up.

Every so often in the 13.8-billion-year universe story, crises have arisen. Had there been an outside observer, he would have been sure the story was about to end each time, but it didn't. The universe always, almost magically, found just the right solution at just the right moment to keep its journey moving forward. In this book I will tell the universe story as a series of miracles where the universe always, at the last minute, figures a way out of its mess.

And here we are again, at another crisis in the universe story, one brought on by ourselves. And here is the universe trying to connect with us to show us the way out of this predicament. But most of us aren't listening. We have tuned out. We are too caught up in our lives and our personal issues to pay attention.

But time is getting short and we have to start listening. We have to plug ourselves back into that cosmic wisdom that has solved every crisis up to now, and we have to use its intelligence to solve our current crisis.

But this requires that we open up to that possibility, and to do that we have to rekindle the child-like wonder of the universe we once had. I know that is hard to do. We have been hurt and lied to in the past, and it is hard to trust again. But we need to think of our children and grandchildren and ask, Isn't it worth the risk to try just one more time?

What if this notion of an inner journey toward cosmic wisdom is just another con job? What have you really lost? You just go back to your old worldview with even more justification for your cynical perspective. But what if it isn't a con job? What if it's authentic? What if it's not only true, but leads us to solve yet another crisis in the universe story? And, on top of all that, what if it takes away our cynicism and pain and replaces them with a new sense of fulfillment and connection to everything and everyone around us. Wow! Wouldn't that be worth it?

I'm not asking you to consider this on faith alone. The purpose of this short book is to give you evidence that what I'm saying is true. I'm going to go through parts of the universe story and point out some of the "miracles" that have occurred along the way to demonstrate my point. Clearly, some can be explained away as mere coincidence, but when you put them all together, it is hard to accept they could all be coincidences or just dumb good luck.

Seeing the world as miraculous leads us to believe something else is going on, something magical. There does seem to be an intelligence embedded in the creative process of the universe that is guiding it forward. We can tap into this cosmic wisdom and realize that we are the latest creation of the universe, and see how the universe must work through us if it wants our story to continue. Our re-integration with the universe would be the perfect marriage to give birth to the next stage of evolution

So that is why I wrote this book—to persuade you to see the universe as magical.

It is alarming to see the climate change problem growing worse and worse, threatening our very ability to live on this planet. And climate change doesn't get the attention it deserves. It's like watching little kids playing on train tracks with a locomotive bearing down on them, and nobody seems to care.

Having said all that, I want you to know this is a positive, uplifting book. Obviously, we do have to lay out the problem, which is painful, but if we are strong enough to handle this truth, then both individually and collectively, doors of opportunity will open.

Climate change is here to warn us: "Change or else!" I say let's heed that warning and avoid the "or else" part. We don't have a choice here. The "or else" is going to become a reality if we do nothing. In fact, it already has.

But as I said, this book is positive. After all, it is titled *The Magical Universe* and that sounds upbeat, doesn't it? Maybe even a little hopeful and it is that too. I want to go so far as to say that the loss of our view of the universe as magical is a significant cause of our current problems.

The modern worldview of science and reason has done many marvelous things for us. It has made many of our lives better and more comfortable through improved technology and medicine, to cite a couple of examples. Also, we have used our reason to poke holes in ideas that lack evidential support, like the notion that the universe is 6,000 years old, that evolution is a myth, and that humans and dinosaurs roamed the Earth together.

We now have to come up with scientific evidence and reasons if we want people to take our ideas seriously.

Now maybe you're thinking that science and reason have pretty much dispensed with any notion of our universe being magical. I would reply "Yes and no."

Certainly "yes" in the sense of magical stories of gods living on Mount Olympus or shape-shifting into other creatures. But no, because, as great as they are, science and reason have their limits. They can't, for instance, explain the beauty of a flower or the touch of a loved one. They can't tell us why we are here and what our purpose is.

You see, I believe we must embrace the modern worldview of science and reason, but we also must transcend it. "Include and transcend" is the way Integral Theory philosopher Ken Wilber puts it.

So, the idea behind *The Magical Universe* is for us to see everything from a new perspective so we can see the magic in it. And, because we are an integral part of the universe, we can become aware of the magical universe in ourselves also. When we realize this, then we might think that this life we have here is worth saving.

So hitch up your britches and get ready for the ride of your life as you enter into the Magical Universe.

CHAPTER ONE

Our Terrible Problem

The Problem

This is the most challenging chapter to read because it lays out the problem, and the problem is terrible. We are talking about the end of civilization as we know it, and that reality is getting closer and closer every day.

I know just reading that makes you want to put the book down and run away. Who wants to dwell on this? It can ruin a nice day, maybe even a week or longer if you let it. No, you might say to yourself, that is for others to deal with. But, you see, that is the problem. The "others" aren't dealing with it because they are being flooded with money from people who benefit from things remaining the same.

So as you read through this painful section, I suggest that you read this chapter with your heart and not your head. For now, ignore those rantings of your mind and just feel this section with your heart. Feel the pain, the helplessness, the disorientation, the fragmentation, the alienation, the hopelessness, and so on. Just let the pain come and be with it. Don't be afraid of the feelings and thoughts that might arise. Cry if you need to. Lie down on your bed, kick your feet and scream into your pillow. Get it out of you because there is a far grander feeling on the other side—which is your Self, your true Self—and that true Self will know what you need to do.

I know there are lots of problems in the world. There is racism, sexism, homophobia, income inequality, war, violence, hunger, and poverty among others. But there is one problem that stands above all of them, and that's climate change.

All of the other problems are solvable if we have a change of perspective, attitude, and will, but climate change is different. It has *tipping points* the others don't have. Tipping points are evolving features in a system where a new threshold is reached, leading to unique and uncontrollable circumstances.

A typical example of a tipping point is leaning back in your chair. If you continue to lean farther and farther back, you will reach a tipping point where your center of gravity shifts and you will no longer be able to stop yourself from falling over backward. That is similar to climate change. Certain climate events can reach tipping points, triggering a new reality where incidents will spin out of control, and nothing anyone can do will stop them.

Scientists believe there are more than fifty tipping points right now in our environment. Fifty! Here are just a couple of examples.

Arctic Ice Melting

This is the most obvious one. Large sheets of Arctic white ice reflect the sun's heat and energy back into space. As temperatures on Earth increase, the problem compounds as more ice melts exposing more of the dark blue water underneath, which, rather than reflecting the heat and energy back into space, absorbs it. This heats the ocean. A warmer ocean causes more ice to melt, exposing more dark blue water, which absorbs more heat, and so on. As the Arctic warms, it will profoundly affect the weather patterns for the entire planet, as we are seeing with the polar vortex, the cold air flow that escapes from the polar regions and turns other areas frigidly cold.

Permafrost Melting

Permafrost is soil, rock, or sediment that has been frozen for at least two years. There is a vast expanse of permafrost that formed eleven thousand years ago in the peat bogs in Siberia and Alaska. These peat bogs house vast amounts of methane, a greenhouse gas that is twenty-four to eighty times more potent at trapping gas (and thereby heat) than carbon. Over the last forty years, these bogs have begun to thaw, releasing their methane into the atmosphere. As more methane gets released, the climate heats up, melting more permafrost, releasing more methane, and so on. There are seventy billion tons of methane in just this area alone, and two trillion tons of carbon in peat bogs worldwide.

Melting Ice Sheets of Greenland and Antarctica

Greenland and Antarctica are home to the two biggest blocks of ice on Earth. A collapse of both would cause sea levels to rise forty feet, flooding many cities, seaports, agricultural areas, and wetlands, affecting hundreds of millions if not billions of people. As temperatures increase, these ice sheets are melting with increasing rapidity—30 percent faster than they were a decade ago. The more carbon we put into the atmosphere, the faster these ice sheets melt, potentially causing massive devastation.

Amazon Rainforest

We like to think of the Amazon rainforest as our savior, operating as a carbon sink, sucking all that nasty carbon out of the atmosphere. But recently, three once-in-a-century-droughts (in 2005, 2010, and 2015-16), not to mention the fires now burning in the Amazon could potentially be turning the Amazon rainforest from a carbon absorber to a carbon emitter. This was the conclusion of a study by the National Academy of Sciences in 2015.[2] The study found that rising temperatures are likely to cause widespread drought throughout the Amazon basin. This would cause forests to degrade and release their carbon stores. The feedback loop with rising temperatures causing droughts, killing more trees, which in turn releases more carbon, heating the atmosphere, causing more drought, killing even more trees, and so on is a real threat to our survival.

This threat became much worse with the January 2019 election of Jair Bolsonaro as the President of Brazil. He has removed many of the regulations protecting the rainforest, resulting in the setting of many fires throughout the Amazon.

---

[2]   https://www.washingtonpost.com/news/energy-environment/wp/2015/10/12/climate-change-could-triple-amazon-drought-study-finds/

Those are just a few examples. There are so many more.

We Have Lost Our Way

We as a species and a society have lost our way, and the only way to get whole again is to face up to this potentially gruesome reality and deal with it, first inwardly and then outwardly.

I know it is terrifying to travel inward. We are afraid we will get stuck in our internal pollution if we face it head on, not realizing that eventually we will get through it and reach our bright shining Self. That is what happens on our inner journey to confront climate change. In doing this, we will not only liberate ourselves, but also be on our way to solving climate change and all the other problems we have because, in the end, those are inner and not outer problems.

Let me repeat this. Our potentially gruesome reality is an inner problem.

Our inner journey is not going to happen overnight. It is a process, but one way to overcome our despair and anguish in dealing with climate change is to get a new view about it. This will lead us to do something to help improve things. Also, just acquiring this new view can calm us down and help us overcome a lot of those negative emotions we feel.

Of course, those negative emotions will not completely disappear. They can't because every time we hear about some climate change disaster or prognostications for the future, we will feel some pain, but the difference now—by gaining this new view—is we won't be afraid of it. We will know we can handle it, using that feeling as energy to fuel our way forward on our path. That pain is necessary to keep us from getting lazy on our way to becoming enlightened and awake citizens, creating an enlightened and awake society. When we are willing to feel that pain then there is no way we won't begin to reverse climate change, and start to solve the many problems we have.

What I am calling for is a new worldview that looks at this universe as magical and filled with miracles.

In the next chapter, I'm going to lay out why I think that is so, and why the universe not only has our back in this endeavor, but actively participates in our unfolding and growth. I will delve into different types of creation stories (ancient and scientific), and compare them to the one I think we need to adopt.

CHAPTER TWO

Points of View

Ken Wilber's Points of View

A big solution to our current dilemma is changing our worldview. We have to see this universe and its creation as magical once again. We have lost our childlike innocence, and we need to get it back.

In order to do this, in order to create a new worldview, we first need a new creation story. At the heart of any worldview is a creation story—a story that tells us how everything, including ourselves, came to be.

There are many creation stories from the fantastical to the scientific. To help us understand and categorize them, I would like first to discuss the three points of view that the Integral theory philosopher, Ken Wilber, labeled as the pre-rational, the rational, and the trans-rational. Then we can categorize the different types of creation stories within that framework.

The Pre-Rational Point of View

So let's begin with the pre-rational view. This view considers reason and science as unimportant. The pre-rational view is based on the faith one has in scripture or anything for that matter. If evidence surfaces that disproves these beliefs, pre-rationalists will ignore it and cling to their beliefs. Fundamentalists of all stripes fall into this category.

The human hunger for meaning and purpose is compelling, and this hunger may explain why fundamentalists refuse to accept the godless and purposeless universe that a purely rational perspective supports. It is too painful for them to view the world in that manner.

The Rational Point of View

The second group are the rationalists, and they embrace science and reason. In fact, they won't believe anything that isn't supported by tangible evidence and logic.

From this point of view, rationalists have disproven the literal interpretation of the many stories, particularly creation stories, in scripture and mythology. But this rebuttal comes at a cost. It not only banishes God from the universe, but more importantly, it banishes meaning and purpose.

Psychologically, how can humans survive in life without having an overriding meaning and purpose in their lives? Perhaps our life-threatening climate change problem is a reflection of this loss. Without meaning and purpose, the material world takes on supreme importance. This leads to a blind using up of resources in search of ever more titillating experiences. This using up is what is threatening our survival on this planet.

The Trans-Rationalist Point of View

The third group are the trans-rationalists. They also accept reason and science as necessary, but they also understand their limits in answering the big questions such as: Who am I? Where did I come from? What is my purpose?

So the trans-rationalists will use reason and evidence as far they go, but they don't believe they go far enough. In short, the trans-rationalists want to synthesize the two previous positions. They want to combine the meaning and purpose of the pre-rationalists with the scientific knowledge of the rationalists.

Some people, Wilber claims, often confuse the pre-rationalists with the trans-rationalists because both criticize science and reason. But if you have followed the above discussion, you can see for yourself why these two viewpoints are entirely different. A trans-rationalist would never accept any worldview that science has disproven, whereas a pre-rationalist would.

Creation Stories and Ways of Knowing

So now let's take the various creation stories we know, or at least have heard about, and relate them to the three domains we just outlined: the pre-rational, the rational, and the trans-rational. I'm guessing you might already know where this is going.

Many of our ancient mythological creation stories—from the Indian to the Chinese, Hindu, Mesopotamian, Greek, Egyptian, and Biblical—appeal to those who fall into the pre-rational camp—they believe the stories are literally true.

One problem with having this view is that there are so many creation stories that it would be impossible for them all to be true. Also if we look at the biblical creation story, we are looking at a world that is about 6,000 years old where dinosaurs and humans roamed the Earth together, and we know that isn't true.

Our modern scientific creation story of a Big Bang occurring some 13.8 billion years ago, with the universe slowly evolving to its present state, would fit into the rationalist's perspective. There is plenty of evidence to support this view. As far as scientific theories go, there are none stronger than the belief that the universe began with a Big Bang 13.8 billion years ago, and slowly evolved to its present state.

Now the third perspective, the trans-rationalist does embrace the rationalist view. It accepts the science related to it. It doesn't accept as literally true any of the ancient creation stories already mentioned.

However, the trans-rationalist perspective believes the rationalist view leaves something out: the answers to questions such as Why am I here? Is there a purpose to it all? Who am I? In short, how do I fit into this whole shebang?

These are areas of study outside the bounds of science because such answers cannot be objectively verified. Purpose and meaning are not quantifiable because they can't be measured and objectively analyzed. So, as a result, scientific rationalism sets them aside, and for the most part, denies their reality.

The trans-rationalist, on the other hand, doesn't want to dismiss these questions. Just because their answers can't be objectively proven doesn't mean they can't be subjectively verified.

The trans-rationalist view embraces other ways of knowing beyond the scientific, rational, and empirical. It gives credence to individual experience in the form of intuition, hunches, gut feelings, revelations, and aha moments. It doesn't mean the trans-rationalist accepts everything that comes through these channels, but it also doesn't mean they reject them outright either.

This kind of subjective knowing, say through intuition or revelation, is a direct experience of knowledge unmediated by anything. The Greeks call this direct experience "gnosis" or "knowing." And while sometimes we can be mistaken about these experiences, at other times, they can be so profound that they open us up to new ways of looking at the world and ourselves, leading us along incredible paths of knowing and creativity. This is the place from which all creative insights emanate because it is here that we can escape from our pre-conceived ideas.

Those who have had these kinds of direct knowing experiences—some call them mystical experiences—swear by this mode of understanding. Of course, the scientists will counter by saying, "Sure.

You think you had this great insight, but how can you prove it?" This is where the rationalist is right; it is not verifiable in an objective sense because it is a subjective experience.

If for example, I have a direct experience with the Transcendent, with God or Spirit or however you might identify it, how can I prove that objectively to someone? I can't. It's impossible to provide direct scientific evidence for something that isn't scientifically measurable.

The best I can do is to counsel this person to first to have an open mind, and then to meditate in order to cultivate an inner state of awareness where, just maybe, they too could have their own full-blown mystical experience. When that happens, then they will "know" and it won't be because I proved it to them in any objective sense, but rather because they cultivated their own subjective experience, and that confirmed it for them.

Intentional Evolution

So it is the trans-rationalist perspective that gives birth to what I call *Intentional Evolution*. I believe that behind the evolutionary movement in the universe is an embedded intelligence that has been working its way forward from the Big Bang to our present state and beyond.

Climate change and all the other problems on Earth are the result of a stagnant worldview that is blocking the natural evolution of the universe. This needs to change. We need a new worldview that shows that we are part and parcel of this whole evolutionary process. We are the universe's way of becoming aware of itself. We have the unique opportunity and responsibility to move this story forward. Our evolutionary unfolding and development is the universe's unfolding and development.

Let me repeat this. Our evolutionary unfolding and development is the universe's unfolding and development

Unfortunately, this birth of self-awareness is a double-edged sword. We can use it to advance our growth along with the universe's or, as is happening now, we can collapse that self-awareness around ourselves and our egos. This alienates us from other people and we end up fragmenting the world into us-versus-them dichotomies.

It is only when we see and experience that we are all interconnected and part of the same family—which includes all living beings on the planet plus the planet itself—that we become whole.

In the next chapter I will show you specific examples of where and when I believe these miracles have occurred in the 13.8-billion-year universe story. When we recognize the universe's participation in its own development, we will know it can happen again, right here, right now with us.

But first we need to understand that we all came from that infinitesimally tiny singularity that existed before the Big Bang. At a fundamental level we are all part of this story. We were all there at the Big Bang and throughout the universe's subsequent evolution. We have to embrace this interconnected reality in order to deal with our personal and global issues.

CHAPTER THREE

The Creation of Matter

Now we begin our trans-rational universe story. I want to show you glimpses of the magic that the universe has to offer and to let you know these glimpses are constantly available. I can't explain all of the magic in this short book, but in a forthcoming book, *The New Mythology*, I will go into much more detail. This is just a taste. First I want to show you that you have the Big Bang inside you. In short, you are the Big Bang.

When we look at ourselves in a mirror, we see skin, muscles, and tissues—all of it made up of tiny cells. We know that these cells are made up of molecules, which are in turn made up of atoms, once determined to be the basic building blocks of all life, constituting its material substructure. For a long time, many scientists took this to be proof that we were physical beings at our core, and thus a materialistic view of the universe came to dominate the modern world. However, in the early twentieth century, the atom was split, proving that matter was not our fundamental reality. We could go deeper.

It turns out that in the nucleus of every atom are neutrons (without an electrical charge) and protons (with a positive electrical charge). Electrons (with a negative charge) "orbit" around each atom. The electron is deemed to be an elementary particle—we can't subdivide it anymore. But neutrons and protons are made up of various types of quarks, which some scientists believe could be made up of vibrating strings.

By going deeper and deeper into the make-up of our bodies, we see that these tiny vibrating strings take us back to the very beginnings of the universe. These vibrating strings were the first entities, emerging from the singularity which was the dimensionless point from which everything was born. Our bodies are a microcosm of that event. So, in short, we are the Big Bang. The Big Bang is in us. It is us.

Getting back to the bigger picture, there are three main stages in our evolutionary story: the creation of matter, the creation of life, and the creation of consciousness. To be more specific, the third stage is the creation of self-consciousness, because from the magical universe's perspective, consciousness is the basis of the universe.

I'm particularly drawn to the first stage, the creation of matter, because it is here that we can see most clearly the magic at work.

From the modern perspective, matter is just dumb stuff that exists. On its own, it can't do much, but exist. It needs wise humans to give it meaning and value.

But from the magical universe viewpoint, matter exhibits an intelligence that is quite remarkable. We will see it is not just blind stuff banging around in the universe the same way billiard balls mindlessly bounce around a pool table. Instead we will see that matter is imbued with intention.

The First Miracle: The Big Bang

So let's start off with the creation of matter in the Big Bang itself. Some 13.8 billion years ago something was created out of nothing. Just that is pretty magical, like pulling a rabbit out of a hat, only there is no hat. How did it occur? No one knows.

Everything we know about the known and unknown universe is that it was created out of what is called a "singularity," a spaceless, dimensionless point. How small is this singularity? Let's compare it to an atom, which is much larger. How small is an atom? A million atoms can fit inside the period at the end of this sentence. A singularity is much, much smaller than that.

It is in the singularity that all known laws of mathematics and physics break down, and it is out of this infinitesimally small point that both the observed and unobserved universe emerged and continues to emerge. Scientists now tell us that, rather than slowing down as was once thought, the universe's expansion is actually speeding up and nobody knows why.

Scientists say that 96 percent of the universe is made up of dark energy and dark matter and nobody knows what those are either, meaning we only know about 4 percent of the make-up of the universe. How crazy is that? There is so much we don't know.

What caused something to emerge from nothing is a mystery, and since the origin is a mystery that makes the whole universe a mystery. So that's the first miracle—the creation of something out of nothing. Let's now move to the second miracle.

The Second Miracle: Inflation or the Second Big Bang

The funny thing about the Big Bang is that in its initial phase it was too small to have been seen by any interstellar observer, had there been one. Initially, the first Big Bang exploded into the subatomic realm, but no farther. This is why theoretical physicist and cosmologist Alan Guth proposes what he calls an inflationary period or what others call a second Big Bang that occurred 10^{-34} seconds after the original Big Bang. To clarify, that time period can be illustrated as a fraction with a one over a one with 34 zeroes following it. It looks like this:

$$\frac{1}{10,000,000,000,000,000,000,000,000,000,000,000}$$

This second Big Bang only lasted only from 10^{-34} seconds to 10^{-32} which is an incredibly short amount of time. It is so short I don't even know how to figure out how short it is. It's mind-bogglingly short.

But so much happened during that inflationary interval. The universe went from a trillionth the size of a proton to ten times the size of a beach ball. That might not sound like much so let's use astronomer Ken Croswell's analogy.

Croswell asks us to measure the size of the observable universe from one end to the other. He said you would discover some 30 billion light-years of space between the two endpoints. (This measurement is a little dated, but still serves to make our point.) If you count up the inches in that intervening space, you get 10^{28} of them. So in a split second a one-inch-sized universe expanded to the observable universe we have today, but that is not all.

It isn't just that the universe expanded so rapidly in such a short amount of time, but that it did so with such precision. Evolutionary cosmologist Brian Swimme says if the expansion had occurred one-trillionth of a second more slowly, the universe would have collapsed back into the quantum world from which it had come because the gravity between the particles would have been too great to allow it to continue expanding. He also says if the universe had unfurled one-trillionth of a second faster, then the particles would have been too far apart for gravity to cause anything interesting to occur.

So not only does the universe jump from the equivalent size of an inch to the observable universe today in a fraction of a fraction of a fraction of a second, but it does it with one-trillionth-of-a-second's accuracy. A chance occurrence? Maybe. But if it hadn't happened with such precision, we wouldn't be here to admire it today—lucky us.

Another important point is the speed of the expansion. The rate of this expansion exceeded the speed of light at 186,000 miles a second. According to Einstein, nothing can go faster than the speed of light because, at that speed, time stops, so conceivably if you exceed that speed, you will go faster than time itself and that could cause all sorts of problems. You could arrive at places before you set out or you could die before you were born.

However, the speed of light refers to how fast something can travel through space. The Big Bang didn't move through space: instead it created the space it exploded into, and there is apparently no limit for how fast the universe can create space. Just to be clear. The universe did not expand into a space that was already there. At the time of the singularity, there was no space until the universe created it in its expansion—something to think about.

The Third Miracle: The Matter/Anti-Matter Asymmetry

After the universe's inflationary period that took it out of the subatomic realm and into the observable universe of today, another miracle occurred.

The energy that drove the inflationary period reheated the universe and filled it with radiation. As this radiation decayed it formed subatomic particles of matter and anti-matter in pairs. When these opposing particles collided, they annihilated each other. So here is the picture. The universe created subatomic particles of matter and anti-matter in pairs, and they fly off. Later, when they collide with their opposites, they are both destroyed.

Eventually, however, the universe cooled down enough so it no longer had the energy to create these particles, meaning now the only action was the destruction of these opposing particles as they collided with each other. If the particles were created in pairs and destroyed in pairs, it wouldn't have taken long before they were all destroyed and the universe would have been left barren.

But, as Cosmologist Brian Swimme points out, the universe in its infinite wisdom just happened to create an extra particle of matter for every billion particles of anti-matter, meaning for every billion particles of anti-matter produced, the universe created a billion and one particles of matter. When all these particles had destroyed themselves, the universe was left with that one-billionth of extra matter, and it was from these extra particles that our universe and we were created.

Swimme says that had the universe created two extra particles of matter for every billion particles of anti-matter, we might not be here because the gravity would have been too strong. He also says that had the universe created only one additional particle of matter for every two billion particles of anti-matter, the gravity would have been too weak for any future development to occur. Once again our existence is based on the universe acting with the precision of a razor's edge.

The Fourth Miracle: The Creation of the Nuclei

The formation of the nucleus is the fourth miracle, but it is not the mere formation that is miraculous, but the fact it stopped when it did, at Lithium, that is the real miracle. Let me explain.

In the very early universe, the temperature is still too hot for protons and neutrons to bind together to form a stable nucleus. The first binding occurs when the universe cools to a brisk one billion degrees and creates hydrogen, the first element, with one proton. When that proton is combined with a neutron, we get deuterium. When two atoms of deuterium combine we get helium with two neutrons and two protons. Hydrogen and helium are the most prevalent elements in the universe. When another proton attaches itself to helium, lithium is created, ending this creative process.

By this time, the temperature of the universe had become too cool for any more creation, leaving lithium as the most complex creation the universe had to offer. Apparently, the universe was just too exhausted to do any more work. It was finished. Done.

So how did this burned out universe accomplish the creation of everything else?

As we look back, it seems clear that the universe knew exactly what it was doing. It had an intention, and everything was following accordingly.

Swimme makes the point that had the universe unfurled more slowly its temperature would have dropped more slowly, allowing more time for particles beyond lithium to bond, potentially going all the way through the periodic table of elements to iron. Had that occurred, Swimme says, the universe would have spent the rest of its existence creating iron nuclei.

Alternatively, Swimme claims that had the universe unfurled a little more quickly, reducing the window for particles to form, it is possible that not even the lightest particles like hydrogen and helium would have formed. The creation and evolution of our universe depended on these lightest nuclei stabilizing; this was critically important for the emergence of the stars and the first living cells.

The Fifth Miracle: The Creation of the Atom

The creation of the atom is the universe's most magnificent concoction yet. It turns out to be the building block for everything that was to follow. Who could have known that when it first formed? Who could have imagined it would lead to the birth of stars that would light up the universe? Nobody knew this tiny little creation was going to lend itself to these magical endeavors.

Even some scientists are baffled by the creation of the atom itself because it requires some real fine-tuning on the part of the universe. One particle we mentioned briefly is the electron. Thus far, the universe has been too hot and energetic for the negatively charged electron to attach itself to the positively charged nucleus. Though they seem like an ideal match, their relationship will have to wait until the time and temperature is just right.

In the meantime, electrons have been playing another role. They have been colliding with free traveling photons or particles of light. At temperatures above 3,000° C, when an electron hits a photon, it scatters its light, making the universe appear opaque.

The milky hue of such a universe lasted from three minutes to 380,000 years after the Big Bang, a long period of stasis in our early universe's existence. This lull may have led a contemporaneous intergalactic observer to assume our universe's creative potential had been exhausted. Lithium was the best it was going to do. However, the old saying "a watched pot never boils" applies here.

Finally, after 380,000 years, the temperature dropped to a brisk 3,000° C, and something miraculous did happen. Suddenly, there was not enough electromagnetic energy to knock electrons out of the orbit of a nucleus, and they began to hold their orbits, resulting in the first atom, the momentous foundation for the myriad of creations that were to follow.

The positive charge of the proton and the negative charge of the electron balanced each other out perfectly. How could we have expected such an elegant match from this mindless universe? But there we have it: The charges of protons and electrons match exactly, creating electrically neutral atoms, a perfect symmetry upon which our very existence depends.

One of the most important laws of science is the second law of thermodynamics commonly known as the law of entropy, which states, among other things, that eventually everything will fall apart. If that is so, then why is the universe continuing to develop? It seems to violate the law of entropy.

Well, some scientists like the late Stephen Hawking see this fine-tuning in the universe and believe the laws of nature were embedded in the singularity at the beginning. They were encoded there and have controlled the development of the universe ever since.

In his book, *God and the Astronomers*, cosmologist and astronomer Robert Jastrow points out the problem for any Big Bang theorist.

"He has scaled the mountains of ignorance; he is about to conquer the highest peak; just as he pulls himself over the final rock he is greeted by a band of theologians who have been sitting there for centuries."[3]

This quotation implies that the theologians could then ask, "Well, who put those universal laws there?" and answer, "God."

However, Hawking and others have their response. They theorize that perhaps a multi-verse is possible, meaning our universe is not the only universe that has been created. In fact, there could be many, many, many more; maybe even trillions more. And each universe would have its own set of laws embedded in its beginning. Some of these universes may be amenable to life, perhaps in different forms than in our own universe; others may not.

---

[3] Robert Jastrow, *God and the Astronomers* (New York: W. W. Norton & Company, Inc. 1992), p. 107.

From this view, we just happened to get the laws we did and, fortunately for us, they led to our creation. I guess we just got lucky. Fortunate, once again!

Nobody can prove whether Hawking and the other scientists are right. It could be the case that we are after all just a lucky random concoction, and the universe exhibits no more intelligence than a cement block.

But I like to use the method of American philosopher, William James, to resolve these insoluble controversies. He claims that when we can't solve a problem with factual evidence, we should then figure out which viewpoint gives us the greatest "cash value." In other words, which viewpoint gives us the most practical benefits?

Is believing we live in an accidental, random universe with no meaning or purpose preferable to believing in a universe that has intelligence, meaning, and purpose embedded in it? Remember, there is no evidence to prove one view is more accurate than the other. I would suggest the latter is the better view, and would give us the biggest bang for our buck.

This echoes a quote by the great physicist Albert Einstein who said, "there are only two ways to live your life: as though nothing is a miracle or as though everything is a miracle."

It also is in harmony with the Dalai Lama's response to the scientific notion that brains create consciousness and not vice versa. That, he said, "is a metaphysical assumption, not a scientific fact."

The Sixth Miracle: The Supernovas

The supernova is so important, I have to give it some space here. As the universe continued to expand, the atoms, fortunately for us, clumped together in groups. They weren't uniformly distributed throughout the universe. This is known as the lumpy universe, kind of like the lumps in your oatmeal.

The atoms in each of these clumps exerted a gravitational pull on the other atoms in their group, pulling them closer and closer together. As more atoms piled on top of each other, the pressure at the core grew, increasing its heat and energy. Eventually, the pressure caused the heat to reach 10,000,000°C, which fused the hydrogen atoms, thus igniting the first star and lighting up the universe.

In the stars that were big enough, once the heat had fused enough hydrogen, it would begin to fuse helium. In even bigger stars, the pressure would cause temperatures to reach levels high enough to successively fuse carbon, nitrogen, oxygen, and magnesium, eventually creating iron atoms. Since iron cannot fuse with itself to create energy, the process stops here. Iron, which has 26 protons in its nucleus, can withstand extremely high temperatures, but it has its limits. When they are breached the iron core will break apart.

When an iron core shuts down, the star will collapse violently and then very quickly explode out again in a supernova. Most of its mass will be hurled into space and its core will become a neutron star. With all of its atoms crushed into its nucleus, this star becomes extremely dense. A supernova itself is so hot that the rest of the elements in the periodic table can be quickly created. These new elements include gold, silver, lead, and uranium with its 92 protons. When a star goes supernova, it creates an explosion that is so bright that it briefly outshines the galaxy that contains it.

However, if the supernova is large enough, even its core won't hold, leading it to collapse further until it becomes a black hole, another singularity similar to the one we had before the Big Bang. A black hole is so dense that not even light can escape.

That means that almost every element that makes up our bodies and the world around us was created in the belly of these stars. We are made up of the stardust from these massive explosions. It was from one of these star explosions that our sun, solar system, and planets were formed.

CHAPTER FOUR

The Creation of Life

This is perhaps the biggest miracle of all. Scientists are still puzzling over how a bunch of minerals was able to transform itself into a living cell. The greatest minds among us have tried in laboratories to create life from chemicals, but so far they haven't been able to. Are we now to believe that random chance can accomplish something that thus far has eluded our most brilliant scientists? Furthermore, it was those greenhouse gases held in the permafrost that helped set the stage for it.

The Seventh Miracle: The Creation of Life

Of course, we can't blame the scientists for not yet being able to figure out how life was created, because it is a miracle. I know they would deny life's miraculous nature, believing that they just haven't figured it out yet, but I'm not holding my breath. It's a momentous task as we'll see.

Let's recap the last step. A supernova occurred, creating and releasing almost all the essential elements that make up our lives today. It seeded the Earth with the necessities of life, leading to the creation of self-consciousness. But exactly how *life* emerged remains a mystery. In short, how did life come from non-life? It's like asking, how did something come from nothing?

The state of the Earth at its creation was anything but conducive to life. The early Earth was being bombarded continuously with meteors and small planetesimals, (smaller planets or bodies in Earth's orbit) that continually crashed into the Earth, creating boiling temperatures. In fact, it was one of these space objects, about the size of Mars, that crashed into the Earth, dislodging a massive chunk of our planet's crust and hurling it into space. This would become our moon.

At this time, the continents had not yet formed; the only land masses were large volcanoes spewing out harmful gases, giving the early Earth a reddish-brown haze. It looked nothing like the blue pearl it is today. Tidal pools, where some scientists believe life originated, developed on some of these volcanic land masses. But how did *life* happen? The early Earth was not a pleasant place, yet a mere 700 million years later, a short amount of time in cosmic terms, life made its grand entry.

The Miller-Urey Experiment

Some scientists think life might have emerged out of a body of water—a sea—suggesting that perhaps lightning, very abundant on the early Earth and a lot more powerful than today's lightning bolts, could have struck this sea, triggering a reaction that may have led to the creation of complex molecules and, ultimately, to life.

In 1952, this hypothesis was tested in the famous Miller-Urey Experiment. Urey was a graduate student and Miller was his advisor. Together they simulated a version of Earth's early atmosphere comprised of methane, hydrogen, and ammonia. To simulate early lightning, they used an electrode to send an electric current through the chemical mixture. They performed this experiment several times, giving each subsequent experiment more time. The final experiment lasted seven days. What they found was astounding! They produced a reddish-brown sludge that contained several of the twenty essential amino acids—the complex molecules critical for building the proteins vital for life.

Others repeated the Miller-Urey Experiment, altering things here and there, eventually creating all twenty of the amino acids. Amino acids are one of the four groups of complex molecules necessary for life, but which alone are not yet life. The other three are the nucleotides (the basic building blocks of the nucleic acids of RNA and DNA); carbohydrates (sugars); and lipids (fats).

Their results set the world on fire. The creation of life in a test tube seemed just around the corner, and the media was having a field day. But once the excitement settled down, problems appeared.

Some scientists, including geochemists studying the make-up of ancient rocks, suggested that Miller and Urey may have had the composition of the early atmosphere all wrong after all, believing it was not reactive enough to create any amino acids and theorizing that it was mostly nitrogen and carbon dioxide.[4]

Also, while it was an accomplishment to form amino acids in a test tube, it was still a long way off from stringing an average of 200 to 250 amino acids together in the exact sequence required to generate

---

[4] David Christian, *Maps of Time: An Introduction to Big History* (Berkeley and Los Angeles: University of California Press, 2004), p. 96.

a specific protein. In *A Short History of Nearly Everything*, Bill Bryson examines the likelihood of this occurring on its own. He looks at collagen, which is a protein with a precise sequence of 1,055 amino acids, likening it to a slot machine with 1,055 spinning wheels with each wheel having 20 possible choices to represent the 20 different amino acids.

You have a 1-in-20 chance that the correct amino acid will pop up on each spin, and if you get lucky the first time, well then, you only have to do it 1,054 more times consecutively to create collagen. Granted, most amino acid chains are shorter—only 200 to 250 amino acids long—but think of a slot machine with 200 to 250 wheels with 20 possibilities on each wheel. What are the chances that the specific amino acid will show up on each those spinning wheels? How could such precision happen randomly, spontaneously? Bryson leaves the answer to what he calls "the mystery of life".[5]

Again, we may want to change our paradigm and think about the creation of life in terms of intelligent intention. As we have already suggested many times, there are just too many coincidences and fine

---

[5] Bill Bryson, *A Short History of Nearly Everything* (New York: Broadway Books, 2003), p. 288.

tunings to continue to believe it all could have happened accidentally.

One must begin to think about life emerging in a different way. If life, mind, and consciousness were all intended from the beginning, then they must have been as embedded in the singularity as the sunflower is embedded in the sunflower seed, thereby making the jump from non-life to life not so inexplicable after all. It just needed the right environment to manifest itself.

Rather than viewing the creation of life as something incomprehensible, we should, instead, see it as an emergent property in the same way that a butterfly can emerge from a caterpillar.

Most scientists believe life began somewhere in the oceans around 3.8 billion years ago—a short 700 million years after the Earth was created. The first life form was a small one-celled organism, a primitive form of bacteria, called a prokaryote. It was vulnerable. Lacking a nucleus, its DNA was left unprotected as free-floating molecules within its membrane.

Prokaryotes contain no organelles (organs functioning as units inside a cell) within their membranes and they reproduce themselves asexually. They are so tiny that 100,000 of them could fit on the dot of this "i". The first prokaryotes most likely lived near the ocean floor, feeding on various ocean chemicals flowing into their fatty membranes as nourishment and flowing out again as excretion.

The Food Crisis

As these organisms multiplied through mitosis (cell division), they began to deplete the ocean of the nutrients (chemicals) they were feasting on. This created a food crisis with too many organisms chasing a shrinking food supply.[6] These organisms had tapped out their environment. Once again, it looked like life was doomed. How would the universe get out of this predicament? Amazingly, it did.

The Eighth Miracle: Creation of Cyanobacteria and the Oxygen Crisis

About 3.5 billion years ago, just when it looked like the food crisis was going to end the reign of the prokaryotes, the universe did something stupendous. It created a whole new organism that instead of feeding on the chemicals in the ocean took its energy directly from the Sun through photosynthesis,

---

[6] Lynn Margulis and Dorian Sagan, *Microcosmos: Four Billion Years of Microbial Evolution* (Berkeley and Los Angeles: University of California Press, 1986), p. 100.

converting carbon dioxide and water into glucose, and expelling oxygen into the oceans as a byproduct.

This organism, called cyanobacteria, created the Earth's first deadly pollutant in its expulsion of oxygen (O_2) as a waste product. Oxygen destroyed everything it touched. Oxygen, you see, has only four of the eight electrons it needs to fill up its outer orbit so it must go about stealing electrons from other organisms, killing them in the process.

As these cyanobacteria multiplied, so did their waste product (O_2). It spread throughout the oceans, killing most of the other one-celled bacteria existing before it. Eventually, the O_2 combined with all the ocean's matter, creating for the first time free O_2 in the water. About 2.5 billion years ago, the ocean gradually began releasing its excess O_2 into the atmosphere where it accumulated as ozone (O_3). Miraculously, this formed an outer layer of atmosphere protecting the Earth from the most active and harmful of the Sun's radiation. Earth had created a womb in which life could grow.[7]

The universe continually exhibits creativity in solving its problems, but here, with the creation of the ozone layer, it appears to show foresight as well. It

---

[7] Christian, 113-114.

resembles an expectant couple preparing their house and a room for the big day. The universe, now in the form of the Earth Mother Goddess, Gaia, was getting its room ready for our arrival, not only preparing for humans and whatever may succeed us, but also for the very creation of life itself. However, despite creating this protective womb for us, it still had a problem with this deadly O_2 continuing to build up in the atmosphere, ripping apart everything it touched.

Yet, once again, the universe was thinking two steps ahead. The O_2 continued to build up until it comprised 21 percent of the atmosphere, and then, the build-up stopped, just at the perfect level for the creation of life. Any more O_2 would have ignited massive fires, destroying everything, and any less would not have allowed the proper metabolism to generate life.

The Ninth Miracle: Eukaryotes

Around two billion years ago, the universe instituted one of its most significant creations, the eukaryote cell, which is about ten to a thousand times bigger than a prokaryote cell. The largest ones can even be seen with the naked eye. Biologist and evolutionary theorist Lynn Margulis demonstrated that eukaryotes are made up of independent prokaryotes that merged, most likely for protection.[8] When we peer inside a eukaryote cell, we find a host of organelles, each containing their own DNA, thus leading other scientists to also believe they once existed independently as prokaryotes.

Miraculously, one of these organelles, mitochondria, was able to transform the deadly pollutant oxygen into a new and powerful source of energy, fueling the next stages of evolution. The eukaryotes had turned the proverbial lemon into lemonade, taking what appeared to be a curse and turning it into a blessing. Now they were able to flourish in an oxygen-rich environment. Another important organelle inside eukaryotes is chloroplast, which takes energy from sunlight via photosynthesis.

Margulis called the stabilization of O_2 at 21 percent of the atmosphere "a mute consensus reached by the biota millions of years ago; indeed it is a contract still respected today."

In their book *Microcosmos: Four Billion Years of Microbial Evolution*, Lynn Margulis and Dorion Sagan write:

---

[8] Margulis and Sagan, p. 117–119.

The present high, but not too high, level of oxygen in our atmosphere gives the impression of a conscious decision to maintain a balance between danger and opportunity, between risk and benefit. . . . If oxygen levels were a few percent higher, living organisms themselves would spontaneously combust. As oxygen falls a few percent aerobic organisms start to asphyxiate. The biosphere has maintained this happy medium for hundreds of millions of years at least.[9]

Eukaryotes also protect their DNA inside a nucleus that is contained along with its other organelles within a cell membrane. These early eukaryotes not only guarded their DNA but managed to use the extra energy from O_2 to further their development, eventually leading to the creation of the plant, animal, and human kingdoms. Without this transformation from prokaryote to eukaryote, the diversity of life on Earth would not have existed.

Brian Swimme explains:

---

[9] Ibid., p. 111.

> *The eukaryotic cell, the first radically new cre-*
> *ation within the oxygenated Gaian system, is*
> *the single greatest transformation in the entire*
> *history of Earth, only overshadowed by the*
> *emergence of life itself. There are two basic eras*
> *of life: the prokaryotic era from four billion years*
> *ago to two billion years ago; and the eukary-*
> *otic era from two billion years ago onward. The*
> *eukaryotic structure opened up a reign of biologi-*
> *cal creativity bringing forth novelties unimagi-*
> *nable in the Age of Bacteria. Yet it was bacteria*
> *that made it all possible.*[10]

Here is what Margulis and Sagan write of this transformation in their book, *Microcosmos*:

> *The difference between the new cells and the old*
> *prokaryotes in the fossil record looks as drastic*
> *as if the Wright brothers' Kitty Hawk flying*
> *machine had been followed a week later by the*
> *Concorde jet.*[11]

---

[10] Brian Swimme and Thomas Berry, *The Universe Story: From the Primordial Flaring Forth to the Ecozoic Era—A Celebration of the Unfolding of the Cosmos* (New York: Harper Collins, 1992), p. 100.
[11] Margulis and Sagan, p. 115.

This change and diversity became possible when about a billion years ago this cell reproduced itself sexually instead of asexually. Rather than a cell just making duplicate copies of itself, two parents combined their genetic traits through sexual reproduction, thereby creating far more diverse organisms and species. Life, adapting to and using the first great pollutant on Earth, is truly miraculous.

To Summarize

Again, if we look back at all the coincidences that have happened, all the fine tunings that have occurred, we can see it all more clearly from a bigger picture.

There does seem to be an innate intelligence embedded in the creative process of the universe. Time and time again, we ran into situations and predicaments in which the continued growth and development of the universe could easily have stopped. Yet somehow, the universe always found a way forward to keep the story moving.

Continuously, the universe appears to be intelligent and creative at its core, having a direction and a goal that aren't completely clear to us. And now yet again, having backed itself into another corner with no conceivable way out, the universe bursts forth another new creation, cyanobacteria, to deal with this food crisis.

To review these processes, we can go back and list the new creations that kept the universe's story alive. Starting in the quantum world, the creative process used "inflation" to burst itself out of its microscopically tiny universe into a universe we can actually see and measure, and it did this with a speed and a precision that is truly astounding.

Next, it manifested a billionth more particles of matter than anti-matter and used those remaining particles of matter to form nuclei. When the universe looked finished after 380,000 years of virtually no activity, it jumped back into action with the creation of the atom, enabling the emergence of far more complex entities including stars, some leading to supernovas that created virtually all of the necessary elements for the creation of planets and life. We then saw how the universe miraculously transformed a bunch of chemicals into the first living cells. These are only a handful of the miracles the universe has created in its cosmic journey.

CHAPTER FIVE

The Creation of
Self-Consciousness

We now move to the third major stage in our universe story, the creation of self-consciousness. We are presenting evidence of intelligent intention in the universe story. We want to demonstrate that this story has a direction and a purpose, and now the development of consciousness takes center stage.

Not knowing the precise details of early man's self-awareness doesn't alter the aim of this book. In this section, we will explore the next great leap in the universe story (the evolution of consciousness) by exploring its specific stages, showing each one's growth and inevitable decline as each stage must be transcended, preserving what is good and overcoming what is bad.

People like Georg Wilhelm Friedrich Hegel, Karl Marx, and Henri Bergson explored this topic during the nineteenth century, listing the stages of human evolution. In more modern times, Sri Aurobindo, Teilhard de Chardin, Jean Gebser, Don Beck, and Ken Wilber, among others, have continued their work. While there are many ways to parse and parcel the stages of human consciousness and culture, depending on how finely you want to make the distinctions, there is a reasonably strong agreement on the overall structure of this evolution.

For my purposes, I am going to simplify these stages so you can get a feel for how consciousness has developed over time, see where it's headed, and discover where you fit on this journey.

The Archaic Stage

Clearly, consciousness is not as easy to identify as the evolution of matter or life. For one thing, consciousness is not a thing that can be measured. But despite that, we can point out some signposts along the way.

One of the most significant contributions came from child psychologist Jean Piaget. He traced the stages of development in child psychology. This is especially helpful for us as we navigate the early developmental stages of human consciousness in history because there is a parallel here.

When we talk about the development of growing awareness in humans, we have to start at the beginning: the emergence of human consciousness out of animal consciousness and Piaget's work is very helpful.

How did the creation of self-consciousness proceed? In the beginning when there was no self-consciousness, the individual was not aware that she/he had a separate existence from other objects in the environment. In other words, the individual didn't see its body as distinct from the table, the chair, the tree, other people, or any other physical object in the world.

This first stage that we and others are calling the Archaic Stage is equivalent to the *sensory-motor stage* in Piaget's model. Here the infant also has no awareness of itself as a separate physical object. This stage lasts for the first year and a half to two years of a child's life.

The Magical Stage

This moves us up to the next stage in the development of consciousness when the individual begins to realize that their physical body is separate from other physical objects in the world. So, for example, he notices he has a physical existence that's independent of the table, the chair, the tree, and other people. However, there is still an emotional bond to his group or tribe. The tribe's well-being is the individual's well-being. So while there is now physical separation, there is no emotional separation from the group.

At this stage of consciousness, one would never say, "I did this" or "I did that," but rather say, "We did this" and "We did that."

In children, Piaget calls this the *pre-operational stage* and it starts around 15 to 24 months when a child becomes aware of themself as physically separate from the environment and begins to explore the world. This is also a time when a child engages fantasies and has a difficult time separating them from reality.

The Mythical Stage

At this stage, we give birth to the mental self. Here the progression continues. In the previous stage, the individual was able to separate themself physically but not emotionally from their environment. They completely identified emotionally with the group. If they were happy, the group was happy; if they were sad, the group was sad.

At the mythical stage, the individual is now able to detach themselves emotionally from their group, realizing that other people have different experiences and ideas than they do. So for the first time, the individual recognizes the "other" as the other. In other words, humans had developed a mental self that transcended their emotional selves, opening up an inner world that could handle certain concepts and ideas.

The equivalent stage for children in Piaget's model is called the *concrete-operations stage*. This stage begins around six years of age. Developing this inner world represents the first big break with the natural order.

One example of this is an experiment showing a child under the age of six two identical short fat glasses containing equal amounts of water. If you then pour the contents of one of the glasses into a taller, narrower glass, children under six or seven will claim the taller, narrower glass contains more water. Around the age of six or seven, children realize the taller, narrower glass continues to contain the same amount of water as the shorter, fatter one, showing they can hold a concept in their mind, and not be swayed by external factors like the taller glass.[12]

---

[12] http://www.intropsych.com/ch10_development/conservation_experiments.html

This is also the change humanity went through when we left the Paleolithic age of the hunter/gatherer and entered the Neolithic era of the farmer around 10,000 BCE.

This fits in perfectly with what we said earlier about the emergence of the mental self and its newly acquired ability to understand that other people see things differently than we do. For the first time, we became aware of the other as other. We became aware that while we watched them, they watched us.

We became self-conscious and worried about what others might think of us, and thus we began to lose touch with our deeper selves, repressing certain impulses and desires that might make us stand out and less able to fit in.

This led to a period of conformity. As societies grew in size and complexity, leaders felt more order had to be imposed, forcing the vast majority of people to find their place in society and to conform to a hierarchy of relationships.

This stage represents the first big break with the natural order. Humans were losing their connection to the creative intelligence of the universe. The whole universe story up to this point had moved along naturally, guided by a deeper intelligence that had navigated its way through many difficulties.

But now, the universe had created a self-aware creature with an inner life. This changed everything. This person chose to conform to society's demands, thereby cutting themself off from the creative potential of the universe. Symbolically, humanity had left the Garden of Eden and was now on its own.

The Modern Stage

At this modern stage, let's first review Piaget's comparable stage in children. In his previous stage—the concrete-operations stage—we saw that young people between the ages of six and eleven develop a mental self that opens up their inner world, allowing them to retain thoughts about observed physical objects even when they aren't looking at them.

We used the example of the two identical glasses containing equal amounts of water. When the water from one of the glasses is poured into a taller, narrower glass, children under the age of six or seven would claim the taller, narrower glass contained more water than the shorter, fatter one even though they had just witnessed that the two identical glasses contained equal amounts of water. When a child reaches six or seven, they no longer make that mistake anymore.

This brings us to Piaget's next stage in the evolution of consciousness in children, which is called the *formal operations stage*; this occurs between the ages of 11 and 15. At this level, the young person can retain ideas not only about concrete objects but also about concepts. In other words, they are now capable of thinking about thinking, as Ken Wilber points out in his book, *A Brief History of Everything*.

Preteens and young teens can now evaluate the ideas and concepts of other people and authority figures, critically analyzing them based on their reasoning and experience. They no longer have to submissively follow the dictates of others, including their parents or society. They can now evaluate those ideas and decide which are most rational and best for themselves. They can expand their horizons to think critically about the future and its many possibilities.

Of course, despite this new ability, it is important to note that young people at this age have limited life experience from which to make those decisions, but the ability is there.

The same happened with the evolution of consciousness in humanity, which is depicted in the jump from the authoritarianism and faith of the Middle Ages to the reason and individuality of the Modern Age. Humans now questioned beliefs in religion, science, and philosophy and developed their own ideas.

Humanity was experiencing a new freedom with this burst of creativity in the modern stage of consciousness. Old ideas with no rational or empirical support tumbled in the onslaught of this ability to think about thinking. This triggered a new optimism in humanity, believing there was no problem reason couldn't solve. This optimistic view became embodied in the Age of Enlightenment.

I should point out here that as these different stages of consciousness are reached, it doesn't mean everyone in that society is at that particular stage. For example, in this modern age of consciousness, there are also people at the Magical, Mythical, Post-Modern and Integral stages.

More precisely, Ken Wilber, who has spent a lot of time studying this, gives this breakdown for our current society. There is still a very a small percentage of people at the Magical Stage, about 25-30 percent at the Mythical Stage (fundamentalists), roughly 45 percent at the Modern Stage, about 25 percent at the Post Modern Stage, and about 5 percent at the Integral Stage. But to continue with the Modern Stage.

Reason, it was theorized could disengage from the body with all of its emotions and feelings, and view reality from a completely objective standpoint, deriving absolute truths that any open-minded, rational person would agree with. Ultimate truth was just over the mountaintop, and reason was on its way to discover it.

But there were problems. What would happen when people disagreed? How could two seemingly rational people not agree on which solution or idea was more rational? Isn't reason universal? Shouldn't all rational people end up with the same conclusion—the one that's most logical and makes the most sense? Apparently not. It turned out that reason is not the be-all and end-all for humans.

Perhaps this disembodied mind wasn't as disembodied as it was thought to be. After all, how does a detached non-physical mind interact with a physical body anyway? How does the thought, "I want to lift my arm" actually cause my arm to raise? What is the mechanism that makes this happen?

French philosopher and father of modern philosophy, Rene Descartes, who came up with the idea of a separate mind and body, couldn't explain it either. Nobody could. It came to be known as the "Mind/Body" problem in philosophy.

One solution was to eliminate one of those two aspects and that's what some thinkers did. They rejected the non-physical. After all, they reasoned, what is the evidence a non-physical mind exists anyway? You can't measure or quantify it. It's not available to our senses. What does it look like, smell like, or taste like? We have no evidence for it whatsoever, so why continue to believe in such a fantasy?

Doing this makes the solution to the mind-body problem easy. Let's just say both the mind and the body are physical so follow the same rules that all physical objects follow. Case closed.

However, if that is true, and the mind is run by the same deterministic laws that govern the physical universe, wouldn't that make free will an illusion? Wouldn't all of our mental activity be determined by those physical laws, making humans, robots? Our actions would be no freer than a kicked can. The chemical reactions in our brains would cause our actions. For example, somebody would say something to us. This would release chemicals in our brains that would program our response. This in turn would stimulate chemical reactions in their brains, programming their response, and so it would go.

However, in our daily lives, as you may have noticed, our mind and body act fluidly together throughout the day. I don't function as a separate mind dragging around a body like a piece of luggage.

The only time I might experience my mind being separate from my body is when I sit back and contemplate some earlier action of mine. In that case, I would recreate the scene in my mind, observing my actions from a detached perspective, as if I was watching myself in a movie. Then I might try to "objectively" analyze my actions, of course realizing that, as those actions were occurring, I was acting in an integrated manner.

This notion of a pure rational mind, existing apart from the body and its emotions is false. They are interconnected and thus influence each other. By suppressing a part of ourselves, by denying the body and its emotions, we also suppress the hidden assumptions and motivations driving our "objective" reason. Humans, apparently, do not reason as objectively as once thought. This became a problem for the modern mind.

Another problem with the modern view of the mind is that disembodied reason fragments reality. When I reason about something, I separate it off from the whole. In doing this, I lose my holistic view of life. There is nothing wrong with this as a technique to get more precise knowledge and understanding, but we must always remember to plug the new ideas back into the whole and see how they fit. Unfortunately, modern thinkers seldom do this, giving birth to the specialists who, as the philosopher Friedrich Nietzsche said, "crack knowledge like they crack nuts."

Experts in different areas may have no idea how their knowledge integrates back into the whole. As such, the world becomes increasingly fragmented as each specialist works only in his or her domain, oblivious to the work in other domains. There is very little communication across disciplines. The focus on individual trees obscures the view of the forest as a whole.

Humanity which started the modern age with such high hopes of freedom and a coming utopia has now been reduced to being a machine subject to the same physical laws as all other physical objects.

The optimism of the Age of Enlightenment dwindled, as the ugly side effects of the modern perspective began to appear. As time went on, environmental degradation and poverty grew. Factories were reducing humans to assembly-line robots. The promised utopia was becoming a nightmare for many people. What had gone wrong?

The Post-Modern Stage

So the modern stage of consciousness which freed humans from old worn out dogmas and encouraged humans to use reason to question beliefs started with great promise. It led to the optimism of the Age of Enlightenment that claimed there wasn't any problem human reason couldn't solve.

But like all journeys to utopia, potholes appeared on the path. We can see the fallout even today. Poverty is growing as the gap between the haves and have-nots increases. We can see it in the devastation of the environment. The latest environmental report just out claims that by 2030, without drastic reductions in fossil fuel use, life is going to be very difficult on this planet as wildfires, floods, food shortages, extinctions, and dying coral reefs intensify. Something has gone terribly wrong with the modern worldview. We can't continually fragment ourselves and the world without dire consequences.

Now let's take a look at two groups of Post-Modernists, the Romantics and the Existentialists and then look at how Post-Modernism embraces "Multiple Viewpoints."

The Romantics

The fallout from the Modern Worldview gave birth to the nineteenth century Romantic Movement. It challenged the modern view of a disembodied ego viewing life "objectively" and coming up with absolute truths. The Romantics wanted to re-embody the ego and bring emotions and feelings back into the picture. They reveled in profound mystical states of oneness, developing a powerful connection to nature.

They rejected the modern world of progress, preferring their inner states of ecstasy instead. They embraced a harmonic relationship with nature and decried the modern detachment from it. They rejected the humdrum routinized existence of the modern world as emotionless and soul destroying.

But the Romantics went too far in the opposite direction. Sure the emotional highs were great, but what happened when they came down and were once again confronted with the dreary soulless modern world? The Romantics had no answer for that, and thus found adulthood difficult to navigate. Many of their best and highest died early: Keats at 28, Byron at 36, and Shelley at 38.

The Existentialists

This mantel was then picked up by the existential philosophers who also rejected the primacy of reason and the inauthentic life of the modern world. Danish philosopher, Soren Kierkegaard, the first existentialist philosopher, rejected the machine-like efficiency of the modern world with books like *Sickness Unto Death, Fear and Trembling* and *The Concept of Dread*.

His books dealt with issues like dread, despair, anxiety, angst, abandonment, and fear, seeing these emotions as the only authentic responses one could have in the face of such a soulless and mechanized world. Any signs of joy or happiness were signals of bad faith or a retreat back into one's inauthentic and finite self.

Other existentialists followed suit. Nietzsche proclaimed the Death of God. Heidegger thought man could only live authentically in the face of death. Sartre saw man as a useless passion and Camus saw life as absurd. They all saw everything that was wrong with life, but nothing that was right.

Despite their negativity and nihilism, the existentialists represent a critical stage in the growth of consciousness. They saw the inadequacies and falsehoods of our modern way of life, but they couldn't quite see the way forward. They had picked apart and banished the optimism of modernism, but had nothing with which to replace it.

They understood the "freedom from" part of freedom, but they hadn't yet mastered the "freedom to" part. They correctly rejected the temporary, finite self, our ego, but hadn't developed an awareness of the deeper, transcendental self. They understood the temporality of the physical world and turned inward for answers.

They shifted their focus from the biosphere (the living physical world) to the noosphere (the inner mental world). They were like the amphibians that had left one world (the seas) to move to another (the land). The existentialists were moving from the outer world to the inner world. Unfortunately, their inner world turned into a prison for them.

Multiple Viewpoints

We are not just disembodied egos. Instead, as post-modern philosophy postulated, we are embodied egos. We cannot separate ourselves from, well, our-selves—our bodies and our emotions—and survey the world objectively.

As embodied egos, we cannot fully detach our-selves. Our upbringing, race, gender, culture, socio-economic status, sexual orientation, religion, age, and so on, influence who we are and how we view the world. From this standpoint, each one of us is different, coming from different backgrounds with different experiences, thus seeing the world from different perspectives.

From the post-modern perspective, no one view is privileged over another. They all have equal valid-ity. There is no longer an absolute standpoint from which to make judgments. Our views are right for us based on our background and experiences. What might be good for you may not be good for me, and vice versa. No one can tell another how to live or what to believe because we are each unique individuals with different experiences.

In one sense, this was a positive change. Instead of the one right view of the modern world, the one absolute objective standpoint, we now have multiple viewpoints. We now listen to each other because we all have something unique to contribute. As such, we can learn from one another. Your perspective is not mine, but listening to you can broaden my understanding of life.

In short, the positive side of post-modern philosophy is the acceptance of many voices and perspectives. It teaches us to be tolerant of different views, peoples, and cultures. Now we can listen to the ideas of others and accept them as legitimate ways to view the world. Previously suppressed voices are now heard.

However, there is a danger here of everything falling into a kind of relativism where anything goes. Everybody has their view, and it stops there. There is no bridge between the views; in fact, the bridges get drawn up. We accept the rights of other people to their opinions, but that is it. We do not engage them; instead we lock ourselves up into our own little worlds, not wanting to judge or be judged.

The result is we have multiple interpretations of the world. We all live in different worlds, meaning there is no real world out there anymore that connects us. It would be as if a professor assigned a book for the class to read. When finished, each person would have their interpretation of it. They would all be different and equally valid. Even the professor's view would be just another view, no more privileged than his students.

If the author of the book came to class to give the "real" interpretation of the book, that too would just be another view, no more privileged than any other. In short, there would be no "real" book, just multiple interpretations of something with no real existence of its own. We are all just individuals locked up in our own worlds. We have reached an impasse.

This brings the post-modern stage of consciousness to an end, with humanity trapped in seven billion inner prisons. This crisis, like all crises in the universe story, opens the door to the next stage of development, the integral stage, as the journey of consciousness continues and deepens.

We have now reached the point where the outer world disappears into inner subjectivity. We are all trapped in our inner worlds with no connection to anything outside of us, if indeed there is anything outside of us. Maybe it is all just a big dream fantasy created by our minds.

The trip inward was needed, but it came at a cost. We ended up living purely individual lives. We had plunged into the depth of our unconscious and ended up finding hopelessness and despair. There was nothing to hold onto or believe in anymore. All we had was the circling hell of our own thoughts from which we couldn't escape.

The Integral Stage

Fortunately, this is not the end of the story. The situation is similar to a miner digging for gold in a deep mine; only we are digging for something in our minds. We may not know what we are doing, but something in us keeps pushing us onward and forward, deeper and deeper into greater agony and despair.

There may be a part of us that wants to give up, but there is another part that won't let us. We are that gold miner who is exhausted and wants desperately to quit, thinking there is no gold here and only a fool would persist in this folly; but, despite that, something propels him on and he keeps digging. Finally, he strikes something hard. He chips away at it and there it is, a gold nugget with the promise of more to follow.

The same is true for us. If we keep working through all that pain and misery and don't run from it in booze, drugs, consumerism or some other distraction, we too will eventually be rewarded when we strike gold, only in this case that gold will be the ground of being.

We can call that ground God, Spirit, the Sacred, the Tao, Brahman, our Buddha Nature; it doesn't matter. When we strike it, all that pain and agony will wash away leaving us feeling renewed and refreshed as if we had just jumped into a cool mountain lake after a long and exhausting hike.

We will then realize we are not separate beings stuck in our inner hells, but rather we are interconnected with all of life at the deepest level. We will have integrated our minds and bodies with the earth and the cosmos, and entered into the next stage of human consciousness, the Integral Stage, a term coined by philosopher Ken Wilber to denote this most profound stage in human development, a stage a number of us must reach if we are to save the planet from the coming catastrophe.

From this new stage, we see and feel ourselves connected to everything. There is no out there because it is all in here. Life is not dual, but non-dual. We are not a mind separated from a body, but instead, we are a mind-body. There is no separation between mind and body, or us and them. We are all in this together. In short, when we fight others for Earth's limited resources, as we are now doing, we are fighting ourselves.

We have gone from being trapped in our inner unconscious, to breaking through into a collective awareness. We have tapped into the source of life at a level that we all share, not only with other humans but with all of life, including the Earth and the entire cosmos. We have arrived at that place from which all things emanate and to which all things return. We have experienced the ground of being and after that, everything is different, and the universe once again becomes magical.

Next, after having gone through the universe story, I would like to use that understanding to explore two of the most basic questions of life. Who Am I? and What is My Purpose?

CHAPTER SIX

Who Am I?

I Am the Universe

We can answer the question, "Who am I?" by saying, literally, "I am the universe." We are the result of a 13.8-billion-year creative evolutionary process. We have the evolutionary story in us. We have the Big Bang in us. We are the Big Bang and we are the ultimate reality from which the Big Bang emerged.

I know this is quite a bit to accept. We are the latest light beam off that explosion, but each one of us is also a unique expression of that explosion. We all have a role to play in the next stage of evolution.

We are standing on the accomplishments of all that came before us. We are the sub-atomic particles that emerged from the Big Bang because we have those particles in us right now. We are the build-up from those subatomic particles, meaning the nuclei, the atoms, the molecules, the stars, the planets, and the rocks and minerals. It's all in us. We are the cells that split off into the plant, animal, and fungi kingdoms that emerged on this planet. We stand on their accomplishments.

We are the animals that evolved from the water to the land and developed a spinal cord, a nervous system, and eventually a brain. We have inherited a consciousness and developed a self-consciousness that, from all we can tell, is unique in the universe. And we are now evolving through the stages of consciousness we discussed in the last chapter, and now here we are.

We are this whole evolutionary process slowly becoming conscious of itself and understanding who and what it is. If we get real quiet and still inside, we can feel that evolutionary urge continuing to push us forward into deeper states of awareness and understanding, realizing in the end that we are the evolving universe.

Overcoming Our Ego

In the Bible, it says God created us in his image. I like to use the term "Universe" instead. So, in short, we are the Universe. We are the Universe's expression in finite form, and now the Universe is calling us to overcome our finitude and come home. This does not mean going back into fear and ignorance, but forward into wisdom and understanding.

There is a reason Adam and Eve got kicked out of the garden and couldn't return after they ate the fruit. Onward and forward is the call of evolution. We are not being called back, but forward into a new awareness of who and what we are.

We are the Universe seeking to realize its Self through each of us. None of us can contain the whole of creation; it is too much. But together, if we can develop our Universe-given potentialities, we can embody deeper and deeper expressions of this absolute.

This is who we are. The eastern religions know in our hearts, each one of us is God. The Hindus call that point where our deepest self, the Atman, touches ultimate reality, Brahman, the Atman-Brahman, and to touch that is to touch enlightenment. We are that individual Atman (the original *Adam*) seeking Brahman. As said before, we are digging deeper and deeper to find that stream of life to fire up our soul and light up our being.

When we touch our deepest self then we know what it is to come home. We know who we are and why we belong. We are this Atman-Brahman and always have been; most of us just haven't realized it yet. We are ignorant of who we are. We thought we were isolated egos, but we are not. That ego is an illusion created by ourselves to give us security in a world gone mad, but it's a false security, a false god, that will destroy us in the end if we don't transcend it.

It's not that the ego has no purpose. We do need it in our everyday life. It's beneficial. It does give us an identity and a sense of self.

But we have to treat it like our car. Our car serves a useful function, getting us from here to there, but we also have to realize the limitations of our car. Our car is not who we are (although some people might disagree).

Our ego is like that. It's useful in our everyday life, but that's it. It's a tool we use to help us get around, and when it has served its function, we have to be willing to discard it just as we would our car when it's no longer useful.

Self Is Beyond Definition

Nobody can tell you who you are, not even yourself because your true Self is beyond all description and definition. You are too big and magnificent to be put in a box or contained in a concept.

You may claim to know things about yourself. You may believe you are a writer, painter, musician, lawyer, doctor, accountant, or anything else. And if doing those things fills you up then no doubt that's true about you, but it's limited because you are so much more than that. Who knows how long you will be those things, and when you stop fulfilling those roles, then what? Then who are you?

We soon realize that who we are is undefinable. We are a mystery. When we understand that, it frees us. No categories or *isms* will define and imprison us because we transcend all those labels. We are not a can of soup that can be labeled and put on a shelf; we are more than that.

In the Carlos Castaneda books his teacher, the sorcerer don Juan, tells Carlos he must create a fog around himself so people won't be able to label him and put him in a box. If we allow people to do that, then we will eventually be confined to that box. The people in our life may prefer that because then they will know what to expect from us, no surprises. We become as predictable as the sunrise and sunset. But that is no way to live.

Don Juan counsels Carlos to create a fog around himself so there is a mystery about him, and nobody can quite predict what he might do next. Just when people think they have us figured out, we act in a way they would never expect. Over time people will stop trying to put us in a box, realizing they can't because we don't fit in one.

We are naturally free and unpredictable. We don't have to force it on ourselves. If we are living from our center, from who we are, it will happen spontaneously. If we try too hard to be different, our actions will be inauthentic, and this charade will be too exhausting to keep up. But if we realize who we are at our core, it will happen of its own accord.

Sometimes, we may even surprise ourselves with new ideas and behaviors because even our egos will try and control this natural spontaneity because it too wants us in a box. We have to be aware of the possibility that we could be our own worst enemy, and consciously free ourselves to be who we are. This could be a little frightening, but also exciting.

So that is who we are. We are the mystery, the creation, the evolution of the whole thing. We just have to get out of our own way so we can blossom into our true potential.

We are like the acorn that has the oak tree, its future self, within it. We have our future greatness within us; we just have to get out of our own way and let our greatness unfold and manifest.

The universe story exhibits an evolutionary intention and intelligence. It has pushed this development from the Big Bang to Beethoven, and the great thing is, it hasn't stopped. It is still driving us forward.

It is not a thought or an idea but a feeling that tells us we are going in the right direction. We might not feel it all the time, but we know where it is when we need it.

We know we are heading in the right direction because it just feels so darn good to be doing what we are doing. It is then we realize the journey is the destination. Realizing ourselves in the moment is realizing ourselves. This is where we want to be, and we will continue to be here if we keep moving, growing, and developing ourselves.

It is an endless journey to our ultimate Self which is infinite and eternal, and where we get to play in the forever, forever.

CHAPTER SEVEN

Searching for Our Self

What is My Purpose?

How can we tie the search for a purpose into the evolutionary story told in this book?

To begin with, the search for the Self is, in a sense, the search for our purpose. Aristotle tied the two together directly by claiming we can't really know anything, including ourselves, unless we know its purpose. For example, can we define a chair without referring to its purpose as being something to sit on?

So there is a lot of overlap in the two questions Who Am I? and What is My Purpose? because they are both the same journey.

Looking at our universe story, how can we tie purpose into that? Well, for one thing, we can say the universe is our story, so our mission is to connect to that inner evolutionary urge and see what purpose or purposes it reveals to us. From the framework of this book, our purpose is to further evolution by uniquely contributing to it.

The question is, how to do it.

There are many models we can use, but I will focus on four: Joseph Campbell's Hero's Journey motif, the biblical Garden of Eden story, Plato's Allegory of the Cave, and finally the Buddha's Four Noble Truths. As different as these stories may seem, they do have something in common. They push us to develop ourselves and realize our purpose.

Campbell's Hero's Journey

Let's start with Joseph Campbell's Hero's Journey. Campbell lays out seventeen or eighteen stages in this journey, and I highly recommend delving into all of them in his landmark book, *The Hero with a Thousand Faces*. For our purposes, though, we are just going after the gist of this motif here, so we will reduce his stages to three. I will call them The Home, The Departure, and The Return. In fact, all of the examples we use here will follow this structure.

The Home Stage

In the Campbell motif, we begin at home with what I call Home Consciousness. What I mean by this is we grow up in a family and a culture where we inherit a worldview. When we are young, our parents tell us what's what. We take on their views and values. There is little else we can do. Our brains have not yet developed the critical faculty, so we end up being a sponge, soaking up everything they tell us without question. Also, we acquire information from older siblings, friends, teachers, preachers, other family members, the culture and so on.

By the time we reach our late teens, we have accumulated a store of fundamental beliefs and values. This store is so vast we can't possibly remember it all, so it gets pushed down into our subconscious. Despite that, it still acts as a dominant force in our lives, directing us to accept or reject ideas that either agree or disagree with this mostly unconscious worldview. At this stage, we have been programmed like a computer and, like a computer, that programming determines what we think and value.

For many, this programming lasts their entire lives. They never become aware of it, and thus, never leave Home Consciousness. They have the illusion they are free-thinking humans who are autonomous, but nothing could be further from the truth.

However, some people, and in our turbulent times the number is growing, are challenging what they have been taught. Usually, that challenge comes as a result of some misfortune or catastrophe which can be personal or social. Right now the threat of Climate Change and the recent murder of George Floyd are waking people up. Whatever the cause, something has led us to begin to question our basic set of beliefs. In short, we begin to question our programming.

The Departure Stage

Our questions mark our departure stage. It could be the departure entails a real departure from home, family, and friends. Maybe we move, take a job somewhere else, perhaps even overseas. Something takes us away from all we have known into something new, where people don't know us and we can begin to cultivate a new self with a new perspective.

This can be a trying time. Leaving home is scary, venturing out on our own into an unknown future. There might be times when we are bored or lonely as we work to build up our new life. We may be tempted, at times, to pack it all in and return home where it's safe, secure and familiar. Some may even do that, but others will stick it out despite the pain and isolation. Something in us won't let us turn back. It is pushing us forward into more chaos and fear.

Despite all that confusion and negativity, we somehow intuit that this is the way forward and we have to stick with it. We can see it as a rite of passage. It's like the Coming of Age ceremonies in indigenous cultures where the young man must go out, undergo some ordeal that changes him from a boy to a man, and then return to society a new person who understands what his role is. That's what we are doing here.

It could be that our departure doesn't take us away from home because the real departure is a mental, emotional, and spiritual one from the worldview we have inherited. It's difficult to do it at home because everyone around us still views us as our old self. They might not be willing to give us the necessary space to grow; they may fear we will become someone they no longer know.

After having departed for a while, exploring new ideas and deeper states of consciousness, a broader and deeper self begins to emerge. We have a more secure foundation on which to stand, and it is from this new perspective, that our purpose begins to appear.

As I mentioned before, the more we get to know our true self, the more our sense of purpose will become clear. Eventually, it will become vivid enough that we can move to the third stage—the Return.

The Return Stage

The Return could mean that we come back home as a new person with a new sense of self or it could mean a return to society with a new purpose. We have discovered who we are and what we feel compelled to do, so we begin to pursue that—and this pursuit can lead us in many unknown directions, for our purpose is not a static thing, but rather a dynamic evolving process. That is what keeps it fresh and alive.

I made this scenario sound like it is only for those just growing into adulthood, but this is for anyone. A person may not have their home consciousness challenged until they are much older and have worked at a job for five, ten, or more years. At any time, this awakening can hit, telling us that we just can't keep doing what we are doing anymore.

Of course, it is probably easier to begin this journey when we are younger with fewer responsibilities, but it can happen at any time.

So that is the basic pattern—Home, Departure, and Return, and it is this scenario that is the basis for my other three examples. Let's see how it applies to them.

The Garden of Eden Story

The Garden of Eden story is told in the Abrahamic religions (Judaism, Christianity and Islam, the three global faiths that claim the biblical prophet Abraham as their founding figure). It begins at the home stage with Adam and Eve in the garden. Everything is perfect, except of course for the pesky snake who ends up causing all the trouble. It seems as if it was in the cards from the beginning.

The All-Knowing God must have known that by putting that beautiful tree with its luscious fruit in the garden and then commanding Adam and Eve not to eat of it, he was asking a lot, especially when he put that "evil" snake in there to tempt them. If he had wanted them to stay in the garden, why put the tree and the snake there in the first place? The answer is God not only knew Adam and Eve would succumb to temptation, (he is all-knowing after all) but he wanted them to. It was our path to growth and redemption.

So getting kicked out of the garden signifies their departure. God curses them by giving Eve the labor and pain of childbirth and Adam the toil and drudgery of work. This symbolizes the difficulty of the departure stage. It ain't easy. God even puts two angels with flaming swords at the gates of the garden to prevent them from returning. The way is forward into more misery, confusion, and chaos.

This lasts until they rediscover "God" in their hearts—which for our purposes here means knowing our true selves. This sets the stage for the return.

Plato's Allegory of the Cave

The third example is Plato's journey out of the cave. In this allegory, people are in a cave and chained to a seat unable to move their heads or bodies in any way. Behind them, in front of a big fire that they cannot see, figures are paraded, casting shadows on the cave wall in front of them. The prisoners cannot see the figures; they just see their shadows, and since they know nothing else, they think these shadows are real so they discuss and debate them with their fellow prisoners.

This is the home consciousness where one unquestionably sees what one is programmed to see.

Then someone, perhaps a teacher or a philosopher, Plato no doubt was thinking of his teacher Socrates, removes the chains from one of the prisoners. What do these chains represent? They represent our programmed beliefs that keep us enslaved and in darkness. When someone removes them, it means that something or someone has compelled us to question our assumptions.

So the prisoner turns around and sees the objects that are causing the shadows on the wall and becomes confused. He can't immediately process this new information. In short, his mind is being blown. His teacher then pulls him up and out of the darkness of the cave and into the bright sunlight, which further blinds him.

This is the departure stage—the release from the chains and the climb out of the cave. As in the other examples, there is confusion and difficulty. This symbolizes that when we give up one set of beliefs, we don't automatically assume another set. In fact, that is the last thing we want to do.

No, we have to go through a state of chaos and confusion where we no longer know what is right and wrong, up or down. We have to completely lose our bearings. It is a scary but necessary stage to go through. It is so frightening that most people don't want to undertake such a journey, but if we're going to discover our true selves and our purpose, we must take it. This is a period of intense searching.

Finally, after being outside the cave for a while, our eyes adjust to the light, and we begin to see things more clearly. As Plato says, finally we can see the sun and contemplate it. We realize the sun is the source of all there is. This symbolizes ourselves getting in touch with the inner source of everything. Through this, we discover who and what we are, and what our purpose is.

Then Plato says we must return to the cave to try and liberate others no matter what the risk may be. This symbolizes the return.

The Buddha's Four Noble Truths

Our final example is the Four Noble Truths of Buddhism. The home consciousness, in this case, is our ignorance of the first two Noble Truths. The First Noble Truth states that life is suffering and the Second Noble Truth says that the cause of suffering is our selfish desires, our ego, and our attachment to the things of this world.

We live our lives run by our ego, selfish desires, and attachments, and when things go wrong, we suffer. We generally blame others for our suffering—our spouse, our girlfriend or boyfriend, our parents, our siblings, our boss at work, our job, our teachers, and so on. Any and everything else is the cause of our problems. We think that if other people would just get their act together and stop making us suffer, all would be fine.

Eventually, all this suffering takes a toll, and if we are lucky, we may finally realize that we, and not others, are the cause of our misery. We can't control others; we can only control ourselves.

In addition, we realize that everything and everyone in our lives will one day be gone. We begin to understand that when we attach ourselves to temporary things, and everything in this world is temporary, that we will inevitably suffer when we lose them.

Once we understand this, the focus shifts from outer causes of suffering to inner causes, and we ask, "How can I stop myself from suffering?" This leads us to the final two Noble Truths and the departure stage

The Third Noble Truth says the way to eliminate suffering is to overcome our desires, self-centeredness, and attachments. If those are the causes of suffering, then removing them will end suffering.

The question then becomes, "How to do that?" The Fourth Noble Truth is the answer. It says we must follow the Noble Eightfold Path, which means we need to have a complete change of perspective. In short, we have to realize that suffering is the problem, and ending it is our most important goal.

Everything revolves around this change. We have to change the way we talk and act. We have to be mindful when our words and actions hurt people, and we have to look inside and see why we sometimes lash out. We have to cultivate an awareness of that deep inner still point of consciousness and operate from there.

We have to be patient and forgive ourselves when we stumble on the path. Hopefully, we can get a job that is in harmony with this path. And finally, we have to think about and meditate on the path incessantly with a deep mind.

This journey will not be easy. But if we stay with it, an awareness of our deeper self emerges and we begin to climb out of our egos and self-centeredness. We become less attached to things. I know, a lot of people may say, "I don't want to be more detached from friends and family. That seems cold." But looked at correctly, it's not.

In our home consciousness, we tend to take the people in our lives for granted. It is why we can, at times, be so mean to them. We do that because we don't realize at the moment that our time with them is very short in cosmic terms. We unconsciously assume these people will always be there for us, so we take them for granted.

That is why when someone close to us dies suddenly and unexpectedly we feel so much pain. We think about all the bad things we said and did to that person and feel great remorse. Alternatively, we may regret never telling them how much we love them, and realize now it is too late to make amends.

Had we instead realized our time with them was temporary, we would have appreciated and treated them better, so when they did die we would have celebrated their lives and our times together, rather than wallow in regret and guilt which, in the end, is just another ego trip.

So rather than making us more distant and cold, becoming more detached allows us to become even closer to our loved ones. We will have developed a stronger sense of self and accepted, more deeply, the impermanence of everything.

When we finally reach that level of awareness, then we can return as fulfilled humans, knowing who we are and what we want.

So as you can see, all four of those stories carry the same basic framework for discovering our self and our purpose, and we do all this in harmony with the creative potential of the universe. At this point, we might even agree with Socrates that we have nothing to fear, not even death.

The Conclusion

So that's it. That's the Magical Universe. We either embrace it or we suffer the consequences. Ultimately the Magical Universe is the Magical Self that rests in each of us. In short, we are the Magical Universe.

We just need to find the courage to enter and accept it. It is beckoning us. The price of admission is giving up all our preconceived notions and beliefs about who we are.

When we do this, we experience ourselves in a whole new way. Because we no longer fit our thoughts and actions to some preconceived formula or idea, we become free to be ourselves spontaneously. When we do that we will surprise ourselves with the new ideas we come up with and the creative actions we take.

Every day becomes a mystery, never knowing how it will unfold or how we will creatively engage with it. It is from this state that magic happens.

One example from the Universe Story I mentioned earlier is the development of photosynthesis. When the prokaryotes were facing a food crisis, with too many of them chasing a shrinking food supply, a magical transformation took place. All of a sudden instead of getting their energy from chemicals, a new being emerged that could get its energy directly from the Sun.

Who could have predicted such magic? Nobody. It just happened as the magical universe pushed its story forward. At those moments of crises, magic happens, and the same can happen to you if you can learn to live from that creative core in you. When you can do that, magic will emerge as you move forward in life.

This is what the climate change issue is here for. It is here with a gun to our collective heads, telling us to change how we live or die. We are witnessing the greatest crisis humanity has ever faced, and now we know what we have to do to save ourselves, our loved ones, and the planet.

We need to recapture that innocence we once had but from an adult perspective. We have to come home, but in a whole new way. If enough of us can pull this off, and it will not be easy, then we can create some real magic for ourselves and the universe.

May the Universe be with you!

Acknowledgements

As with any endeavor, there are a number of people I would like to thank for helping me write and finish this book.

First off I would like to thank Geoff Affleck who gave me the idea of writing this smaller book. He made me see its importance and helped me through the whole process. He, along with his Facebook community, also gave me great feedback on my book cover and title.

I would also like to thank Dhiana Barnes, my accountability partner in Geoff's Amazon Boot-camp. She and I met each week to encourage and offer advice as we both navigated our way through the book-writing process.

I would like to thank Nina Shoroplova for her invaluable editing assistance and her willingness to work with me step-by-step along the way.

Finally, I would like to thank my wife, Carole McGraw, who read through the manuscript and helped me make it more readable and understandable.

Author Bio

For over twenty years, Bruce McGraw has taught community college courses in San Diego in philosophy, religious studies, humanities, and mythology. He gained his MA in Philosophy and Religious Studies from the University of California at San Diego. He is intrigued by the search to find the core essence—the wisdom—behind the ideas of all the great philosophers and spiritual teachers and applying that understanding to our problems today. His goal is to put all he has learned into an evolutionary framework that explains the history of everything from the Big Bang to now.

Bruce McGraw also helped establish, edit, and write for a local San Diego newspaper. In that endeavor, Bruce won First Place awards from the San Diego Press Club for Best Series, Best Commentary, and Best Science/Environmental Writing.

The Magical Universe sets the stage for McGraw's next book, *The New Mythology: A New Vision for a Troubled Planet.* This is a larger, more comprehensive look at the issues covered in *The Magical Universe.*

Made in the USA
Las Vegas, NV
25 November 2022